AF594623
Jolly Phonics
Handwriting Book 7
qu ou oi ue er ar
in print letters

Guidelines

Good pencil control and correct formation enable students to achieve neat, fluent and, eventually, joined handwriting.

Handwriting practice works best when the students are sitting at their table or desk. This provides a firm flat surface to write on and encourages correct posture.

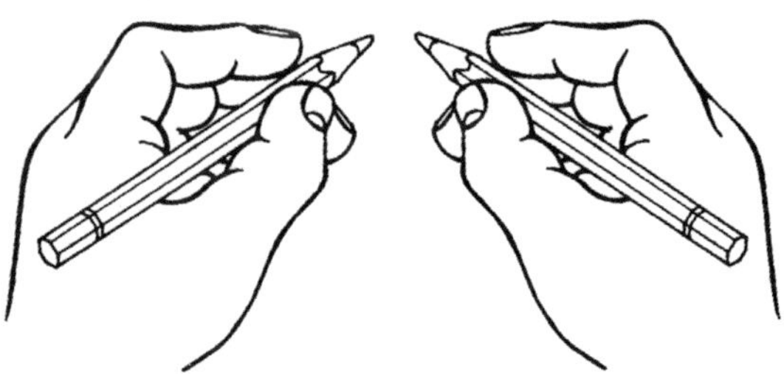

A good pencil hold from the very beginning is extremely important for developing neat, fluent handwriting. The tripod pencil grip is recommended.

Hold the pencil between the thumb and index finger, and support it on the middle finger. As the pencil is moved, the knuckles on the thumb and index finger look like a frog's legs.

Coloring is also a good way to develop fine motor skills. Encourage the students to color carefully, to keep within the lines, and to choose appropriate colors.

Spot the frog

Encourage the children to look out for the frog throughout these books, to remind them to practice their "froggy-leg" grip.

Write your name on the sign and draw you and your family in the windows of the house.

Complete the pictures.

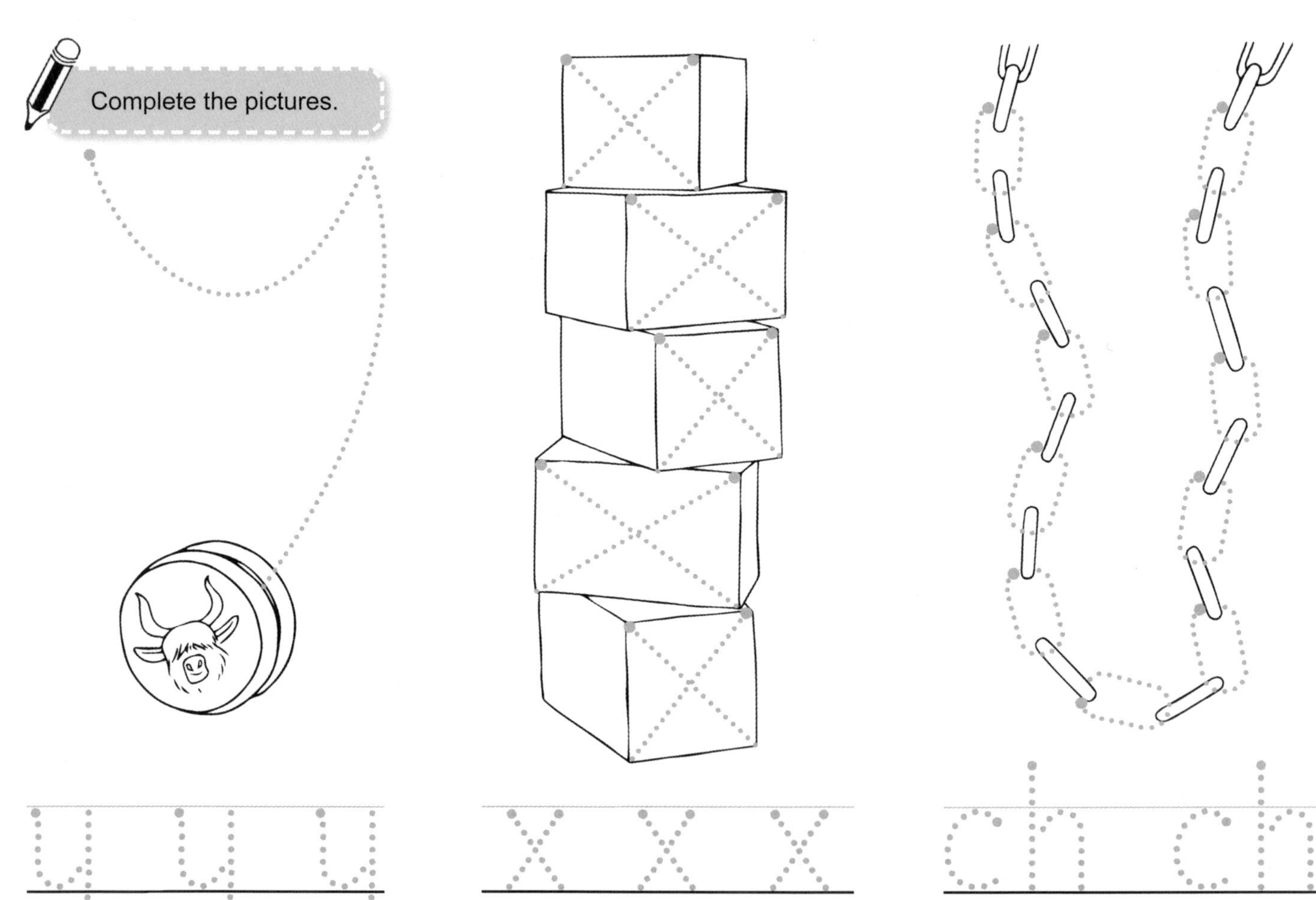

sh sh
th th
th th

1
2
qu
squirrels
qu qu qu

Help the ants write with their quills.

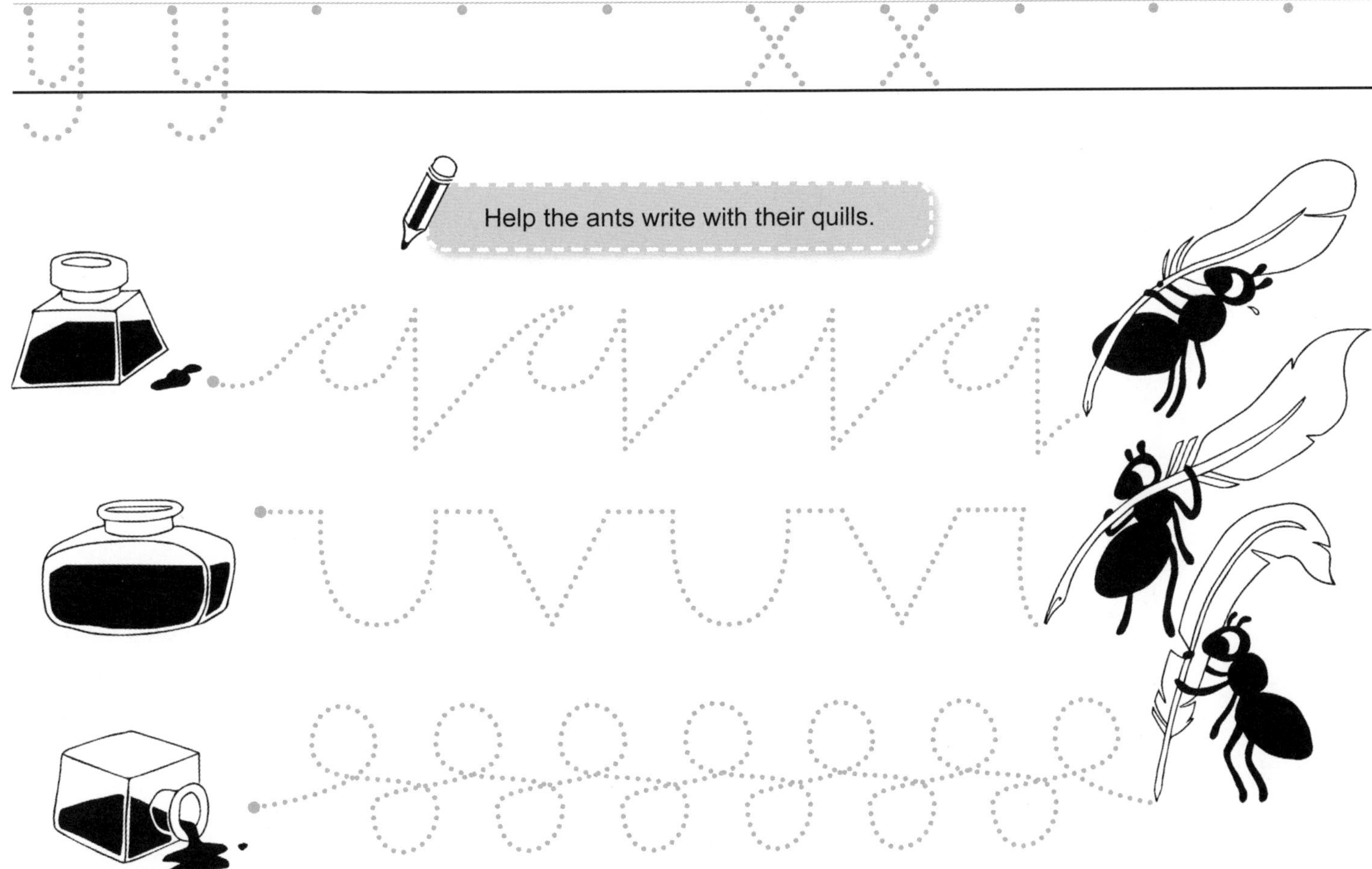

1
2
ou
sprouting
What happened to the frog's finger?
What could he be saying?

ou ou ou

ch sh

Can you see any plants with round leaves in the greenhouse?

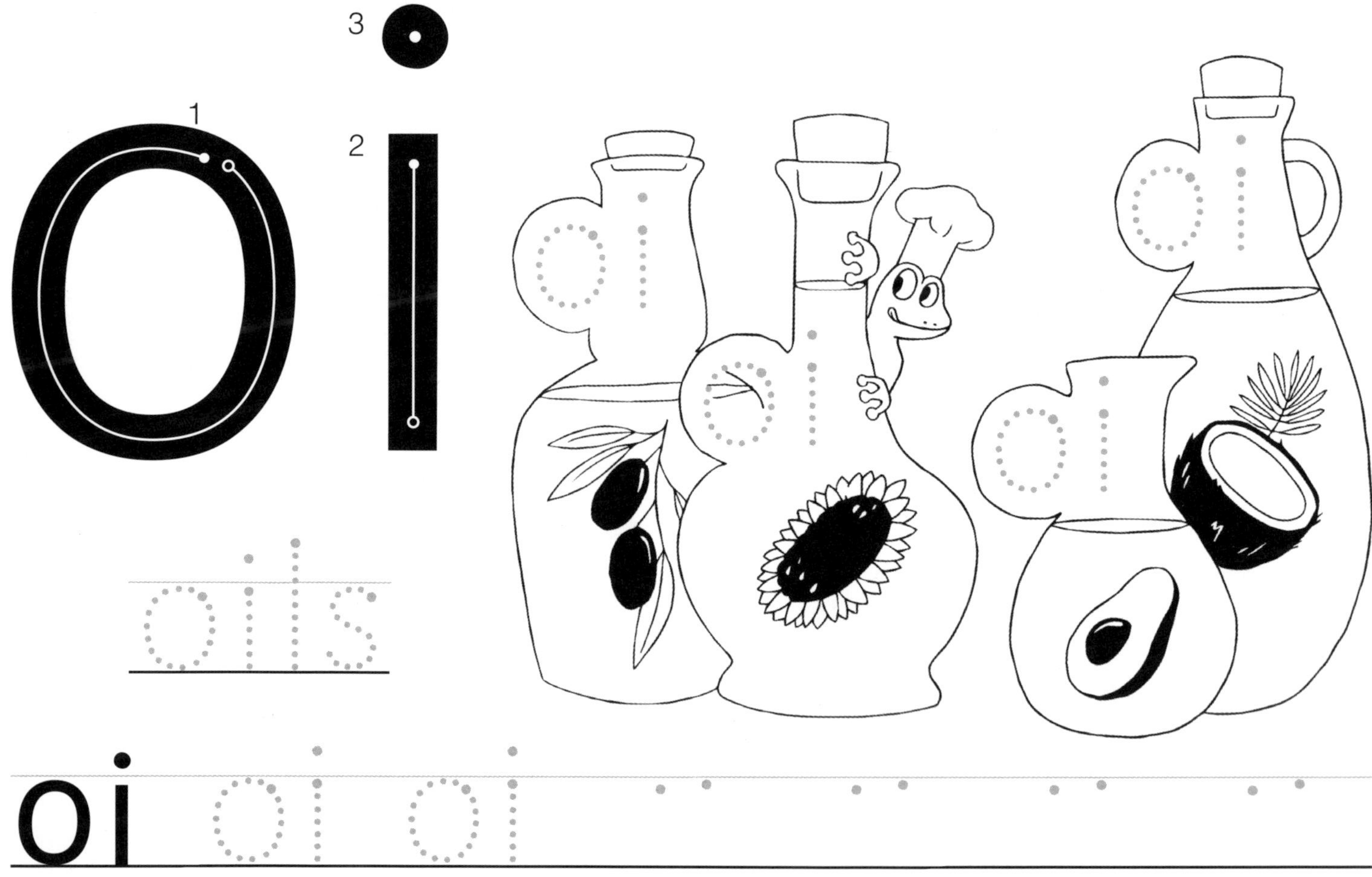

oi oi oi

coins

Trace the paths of the bouncing coins.

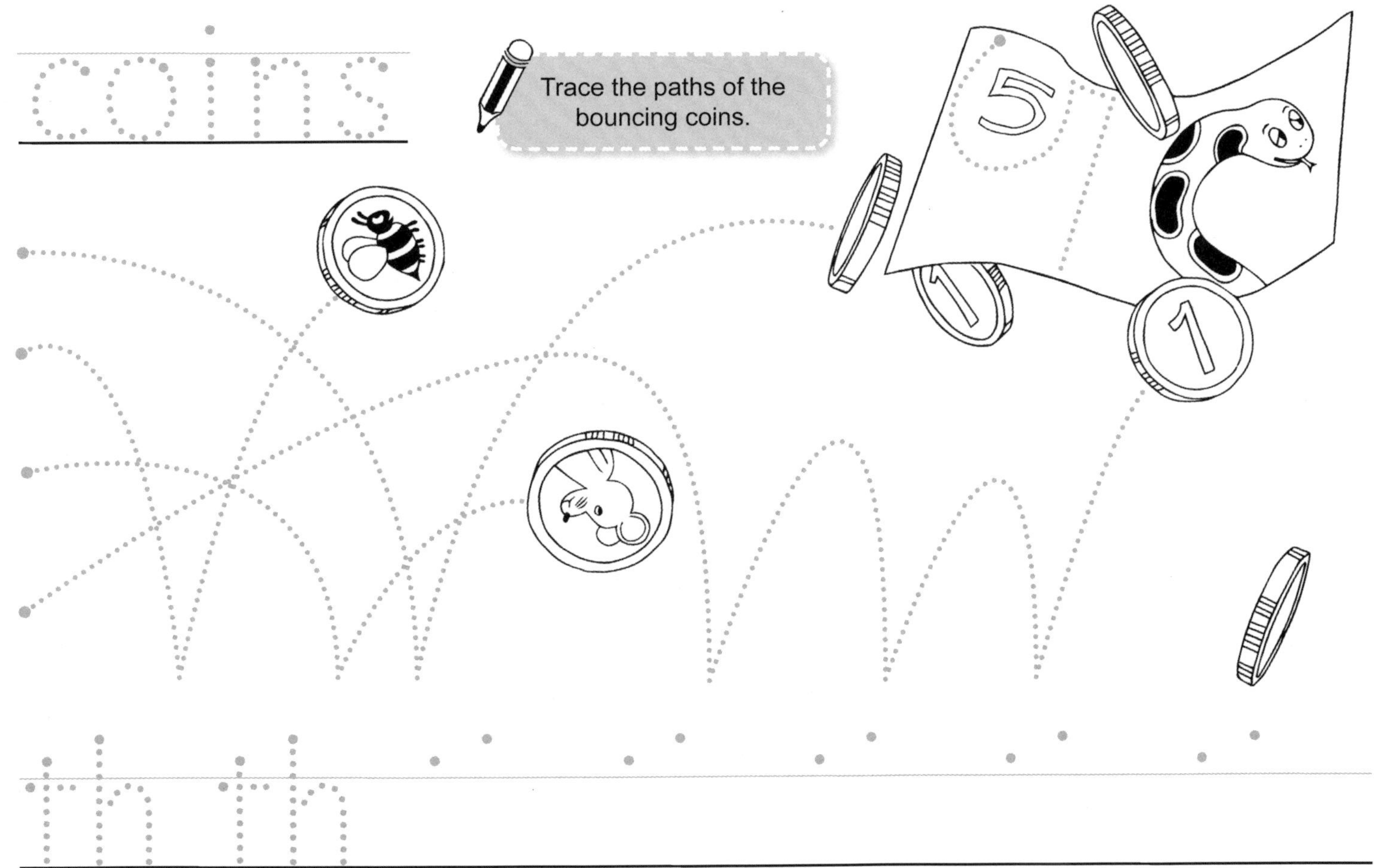

How many of these animals do you know?

Can you point to the squid?

1 u 2 e

Complete the statues.

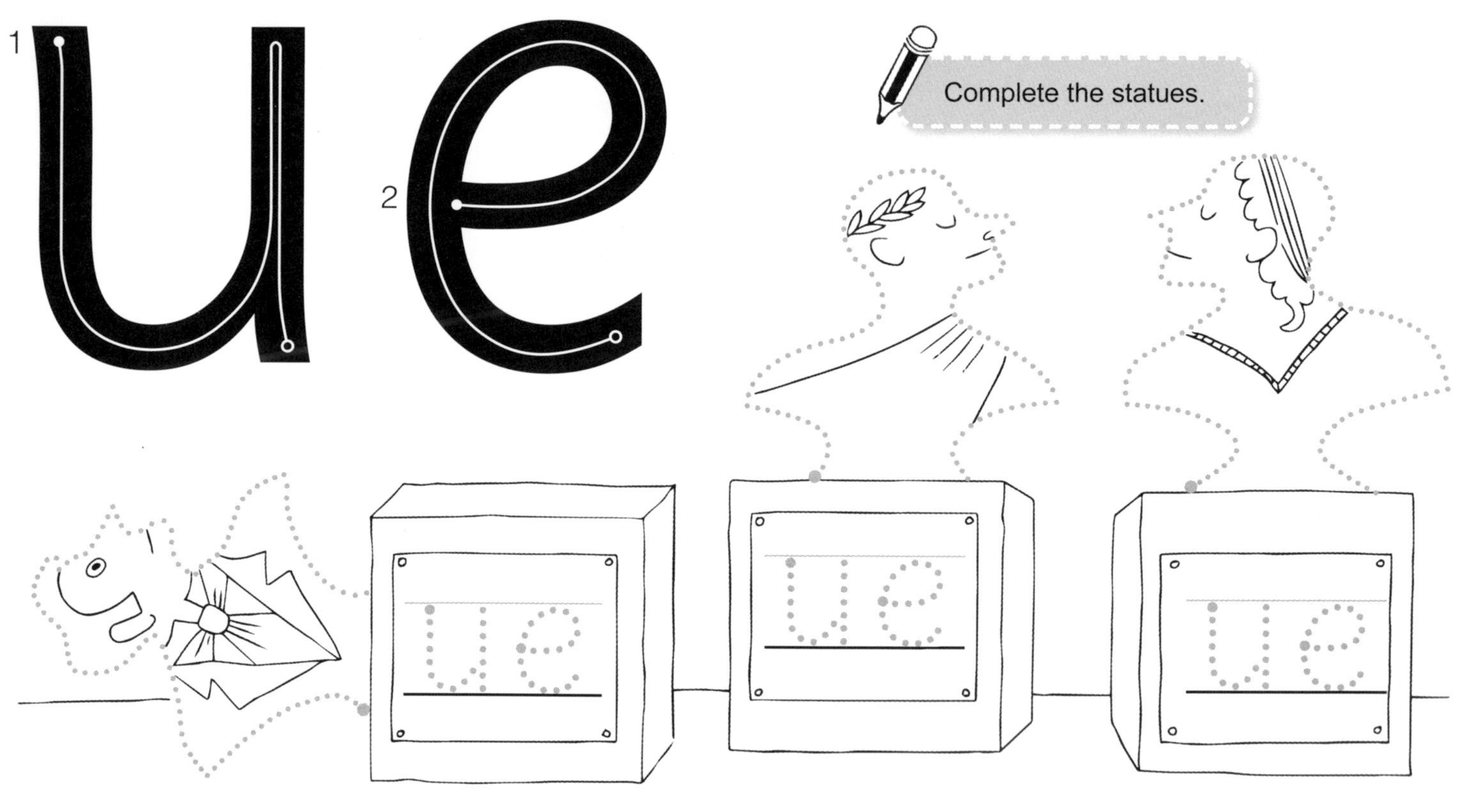

ue

qu qu

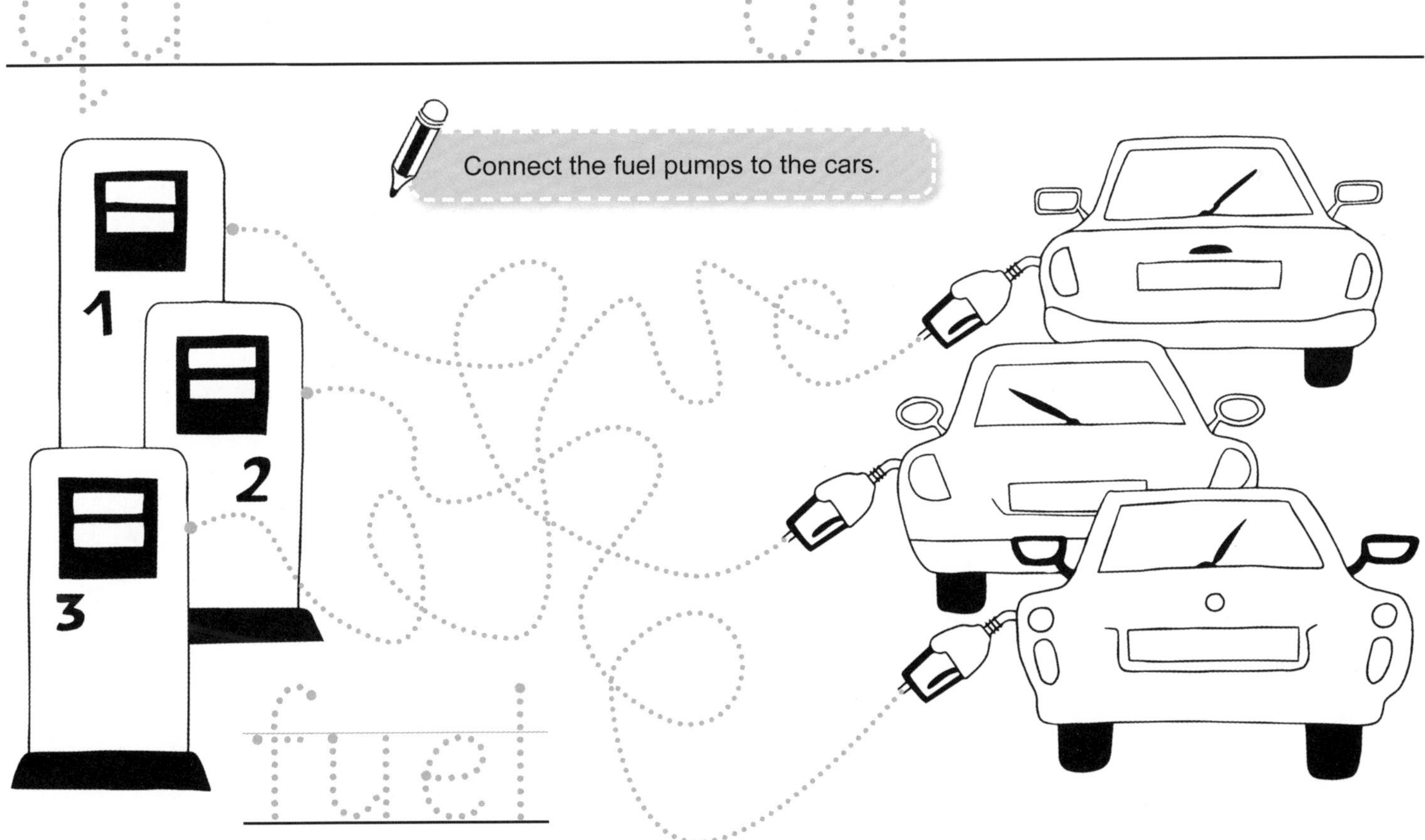

er

oi ue

ar
1
2
Do you know what some armadillos do when they are scared?
ar

er ar

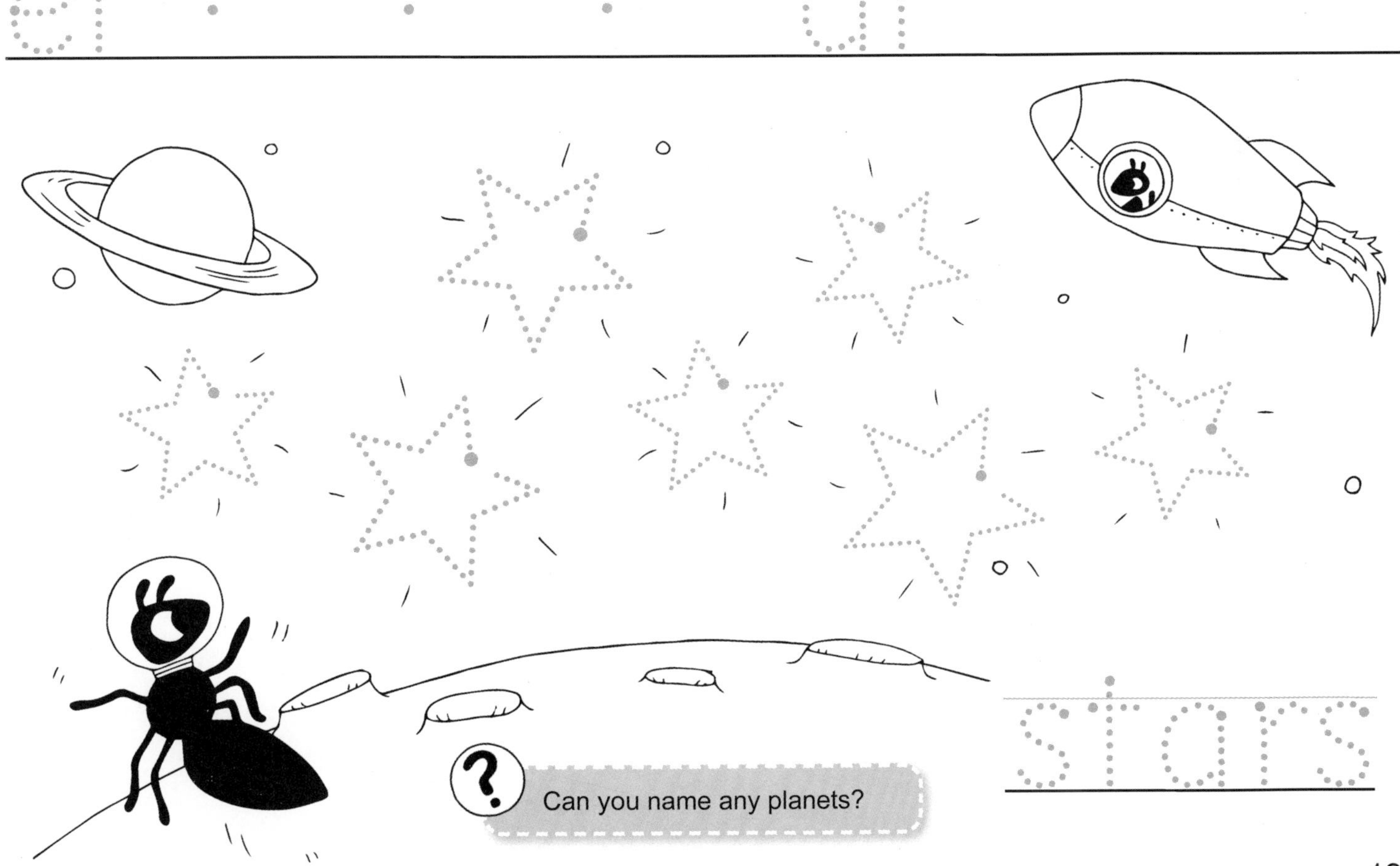

a barbecue
What do you like to cook on a barbecue?
in summer

a blizzard
Where is the snowman's scarf?
in winter

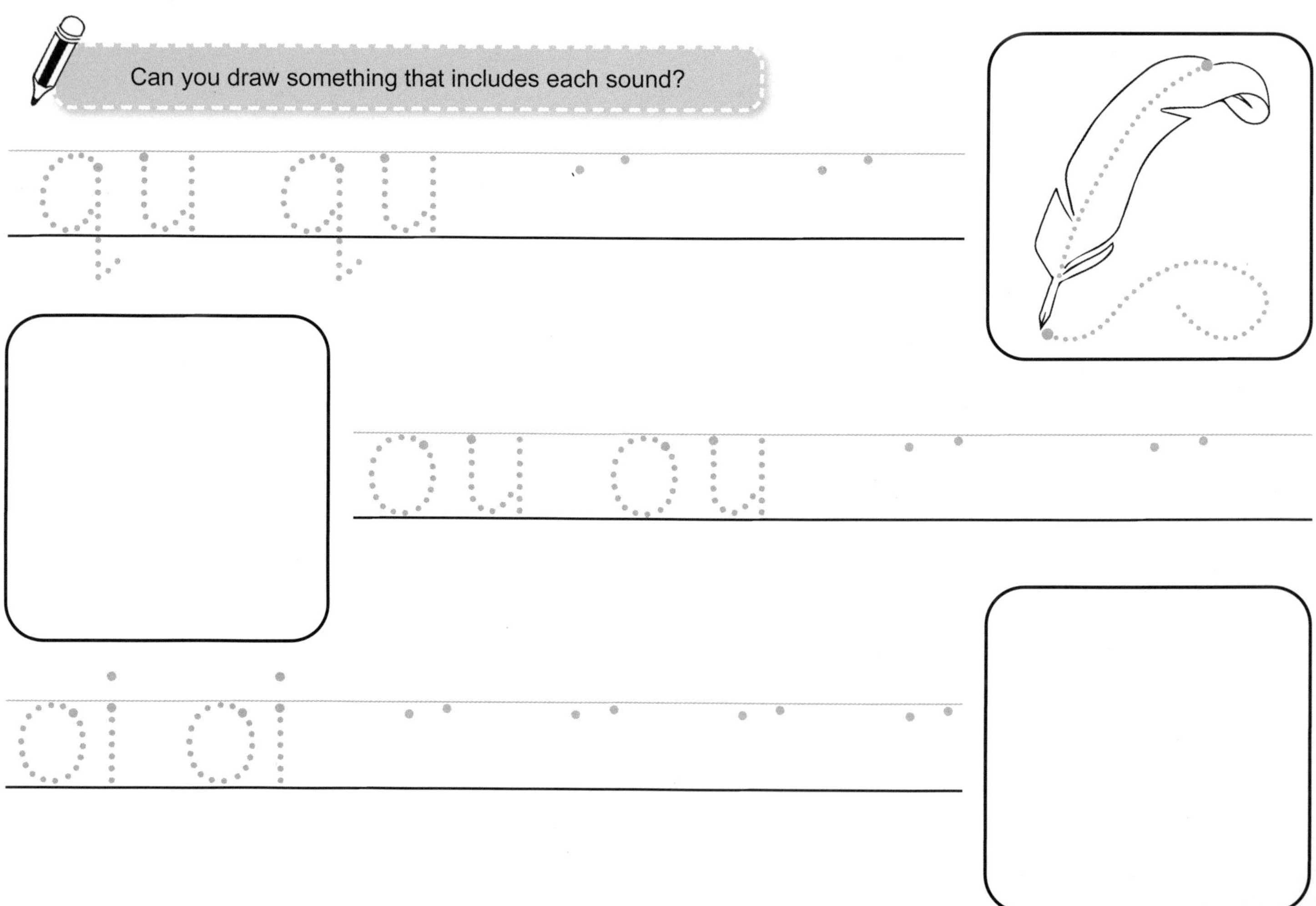
Can you draw something that includes each sound?
qu qu
ou ou
oi oi

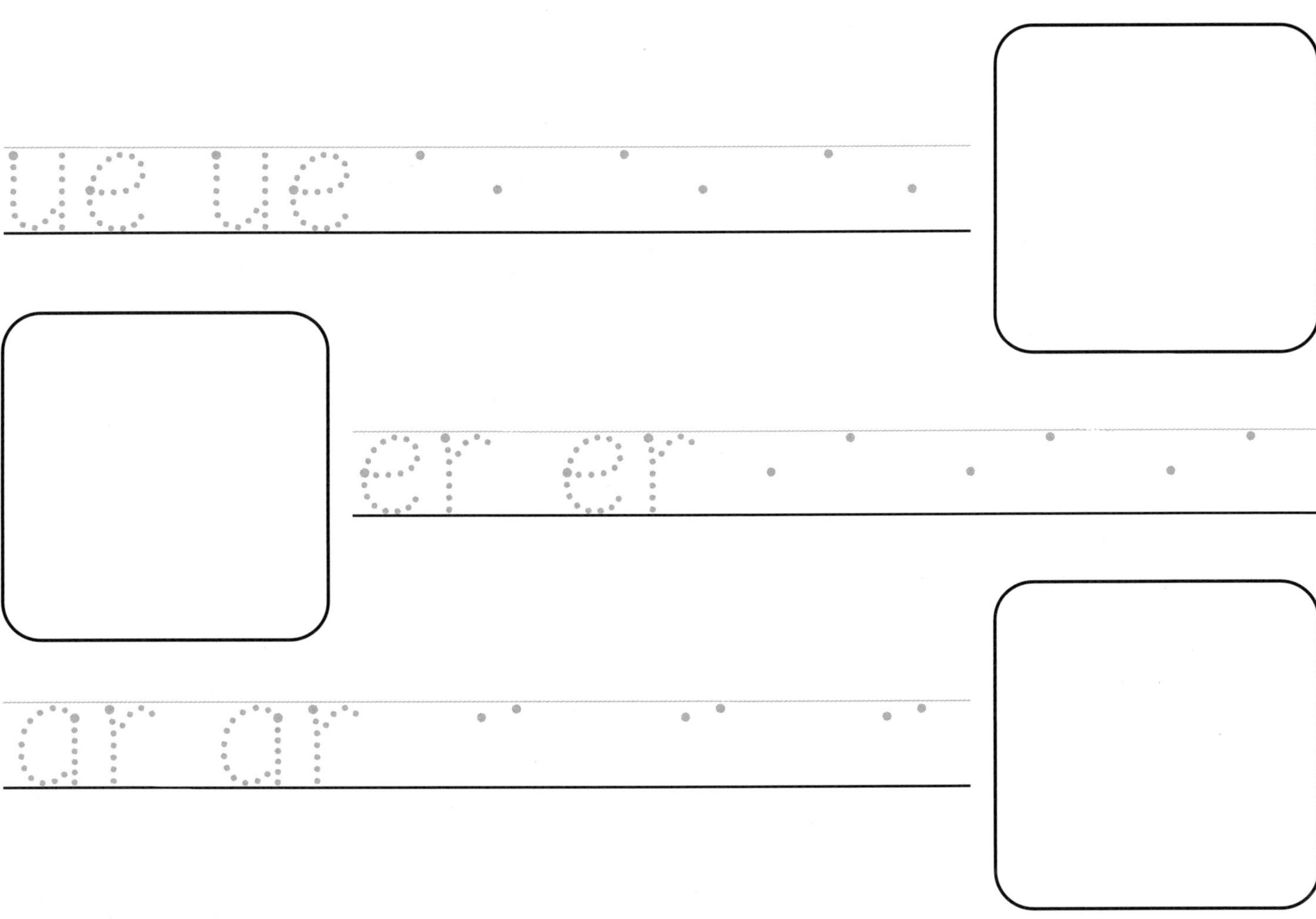
ue ue
er er
ar ar

Ages 4+

Jolly Phonics Handwriting Book

Perfect for practicing letter formation

These handwriting books provide letter formation practice for beginner writers. Dotted letters and words (with starting dots) remind students how the letters are formed, and encourage them to write words using the letter sounds they know.
Each page features fun activities to complete and attractive pictures to color, which help the students to develop fine motor control.

This book contains the following letter sounds:

Group 1:	s a t i p n
Group 2:	c k e h r m d
Group 3:	g o u l f b
Group 4:	ai j oa ie ee or
Group 5:	z w ng v oo oo
Group 6:	y x ch sh th th
Group 7:	qu ou oi ue er ar

To see the full range of Jolly Phonics products, visit our website at www.jollylearning.com

MIX
Paper | Supporting responsible forestry
FSC® C016973

ISBN 978-1-83582-187-9

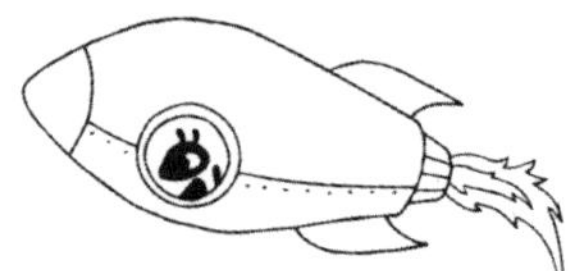

82 Winter Sport Lane, Williston, VT 05495, USA. Tel: +1-800-488-2665
77 Hornbeam Road, Buckhurst Hill, Essex, IG9 6JX, UK. Tel: +44 20 8501 0405
Printed in China.

www.jollylearning.com info@jollylearning.co.uk

Reference: JL1879